BEETLE BAILEY is one of the most successful comic strips in the history of comics. The two people most responsible for the success of BEETLE BAILEY are Beetle himself, and his famous creator, Mort Walker.

Walker's reluctant army private has catapulted to international stardom and popularity. BEETLE BAILEY is syndicated in 1,135 newspapers and enjoyed by over sixty million readers in the United States and fifty other countries.

Mort Walker thinks of Beetle as part of a U.S. army that is primarily made up of civilians. "Beetle is typical of these civilians who never become real soldiers. He resists this unnatural way of life in every way he can."

Mr. Walker's life, on the other hand, is happily natural. He lives and works in Greenwich, Connecticut with his wife, his seven children, and more notable brain children—among them another internationally famous comic strip, HI AND LOIS.

at ease, beetle bailey

by
MORT WALKER

TEMPO
BOOKS

GROSSET AND DUNLAP, INC.
A NATIONAL GENERAL COMPANY
Publishers   NEW YORK

at ease, beetle bailey

TO: General Amos T. Halftrack
Headquarters, Camp Swampy
SUBJECT: Application for typing job.

Dear Sir:
I understand you are looking for a quality typist to work in your tent during maneuvers.

I would like to apply for the job since I am a quality typist. I feel my talents are being wasted as a mere foot-slogging rifleman.

As you can see, my work is neat
and free from errors and erasures.
I pride myself on my unblemished
precision.

yors utrly

11-5

SARGE WENT INTO TOWN, BEETLE

WHY DIDN'T HE SAY SO IN THE FIRST PLACE?

PX

VIDEO TAPE REPLAY

VIDEO TAPE REPLAY

MORT WALKER

7-17

2-26

4-9

2-14

Mort WALKER

LIKE THE TIME I DIDN'T KNOW YOU WERE ON THE ARTILLERY RANGE! HEE HEE!

THINK OF THE MEDICAL CARE YOU'D BE GIVING UP! ALL THAT FREE ASPIRIN!

AND THE CHOW! THERE'S NOT ANOTHER CHEF IN THE WORLD LIKE COOKIE!

THEN THERE'S THE RUGGED OUTDOOR LIFE THAT GIVES A MAN THAT HEALTHY GLOW

HOW COULD YOU LEAVE THIS CITADEL OF CIVILIZATION?!

---THIS HALLOWED GROUND MADE NOBLE BY MILLIONS OF MARCHING FEET

THESE MEN! THE PROMISE OF HEROIC DEEDS SHINES IN THEIR EYES!

HE'S SIGNING UP FOR ANOTHER TEN YEARS

Mort WALKER

9-15

2-10

THEY ARE **SITTING DUCKS!**

8-6

SGT. SNORKEL WILL DEMONSTRATE HOW EVEN OFFICE WORKERS CAN STAY IN SHAPE THROUGH SIMPLE EXERCISES

"Lesson number one: For arms, shoulders, back. While seated at desk..."

"...place fingertips under top of desk..."